A companion volume by the same author: The Discovery of the Square

BRUNO MUNARI
THE DISCOVERY OF THE CIRCLE

GEORGE WITTENBORN INC.
1018 Madison Avenue, New York, N.Y. 10021

352262

While the square is closely connected with man and his constructions, with architecture, building forms, lettering etc., the circle is related to the divine: since ancient times a simple circle has represented eternity, for it has neither beginning nor end. An old text says that God is a circle whose center is everywhere, but whose circumference is nowhere.

The circle is essentially a dynamic figure: it is the basis of all rotary movements, of all vain searches for perpetual motion.

Although it is the simplest of all curves, the circle is considered by mathematicians to be a polygon with an infinite number of sides. Take away an invisible point from the circumference of a circle and it is not a circle any more, but a *pathocircle* which presents complicated problems. A point marked on the circumference of a circle eliminates the idea of eternity by indicating a beginning, and therefore an end, to the circumference itself. If this circle is rolled along a straight line and kept always in the same plane, the point marked on its circumference draws a cycloid. The circle is easily found in nature: we need only to throw a pebble in still water. The sphere, on the other hand, is formed spontaneously in soap bubbles. A tree grows according to a circular, concentric pattern: a section shows its rings. A circle drawn by hand showed Giotto's skill. The first thing that a child draws looks like a circle. People form a circle spontaneously when they want to observe something from nearby, thus giving rise to the arena, the circus, the trading posts on the floor of the stock exchange.

One of the oldest symbols is a disk made of two equal and opposing dynamic parts: Yang-Yin, which represent the balance of opposing forces in every living thing.

Famous painters have painted over a circular surface, each one finding solutions of composition closely bound to the circular form; in some cases, as in the Virgin with Child by Botticelli, the final optical effect of the work is spherical.

A disk laid on a plane cannot be placed in the wrong way, therefore dishes are almost always round: it is simpler to arrange them on the table; if they are hexagonal or square or oval, it would require more care in placing them; without this care they would give a sense of disorder, whereas a circle is always in place. This is even more true of the sphere, which can never be overturned: in any position it is always straight, so to speak.

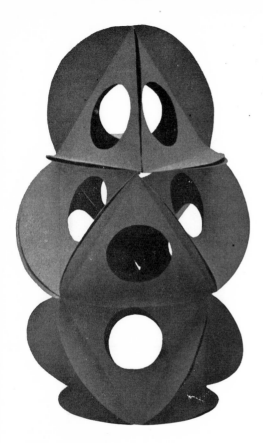

ACONA' BICONBI'

A three dimensional construction obtained by the repetition and union of equal elements in the form of a circular crown. The global form varies according to the number of elements.

AGRIPPA

The magic circle of Agrippa.

AMATERASU

Popular Japanese goddess, dressed in red, standing on a rock with the solar disk in her right hand. According to legend, Amaterasu was born from the right eye of the god Izanagi; as soon as she was born her resplendent beauty lit the whole world and Izanagi granted her the empire of the sun.

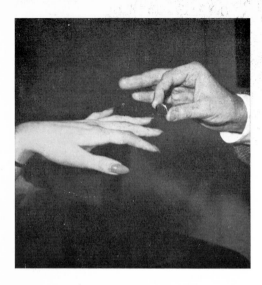

The magic circle of the Archangel Michael.

THE RING

It seems that the origin of the ring is Asiatic. Both Hebrews and Egyptians wore rings. The early Romans wore only iron rings with seals. Gold rings were the sign of people of high rank. In Venice, at the time of Pope Alexander III, every year on the day of the Ascension, the Doges used to throw a ring into the sea as a symbol of the city's marriage to the sea.

GROWTH RINGS

Cross section of a tree trunk.

THE HALO

Portait of St. Francis by Simone Martini, Assisi.

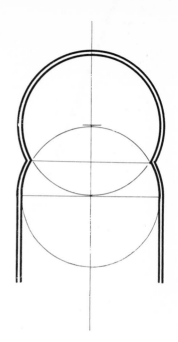

MOSLEM ARCH

Structural outline of the Arabic-Moorish arch.

NEWTON'S RINGS

If a slightly convex lens is put on a flat glass surface and lit by a white light, a series of concentric and iridescent rings appears around the point of contact of the two glasses. If instead of a white light one uses a red one, many regular, distinct rings, alternately red and dark, are formed around the point of contact. The farther out the rings are from the central black spot, the smaller the distance becomes between the rings. Newton discovered that the ratio of the radii of the dark rings is the same as the ratio of the square roots of consecutive even numbers.

TO HAVE FINISHED

In ancient times it was customary after a sacrifice to soak a circle in the altar with the blood of the victims and to pronounce a sacred Greek word meaning *to have finished.*

ANNUAL - BIENNIAL

Botanical signs for annual and biennial plants.

EQUAL AREAS

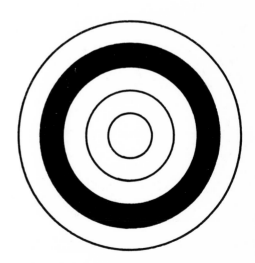

The surface outside the black ring is equal to the surface enclosed by the black ring. The radius is divided into five equal parts.

JAPANESE FLAG

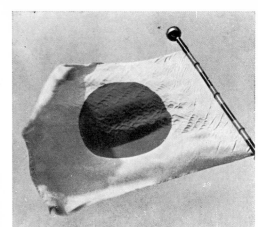

OLYMPIC FLAG

DAVIDE BORIANI

Magnetic surface. Kinetic object shown at the Olivetti exhibition in Milan, May 1962. The object is 32 inches in diameter and contains iron filings which are kept in constant motion by a series of magnets moving in different ways under the surface, thus composing an infinite variety of designs.

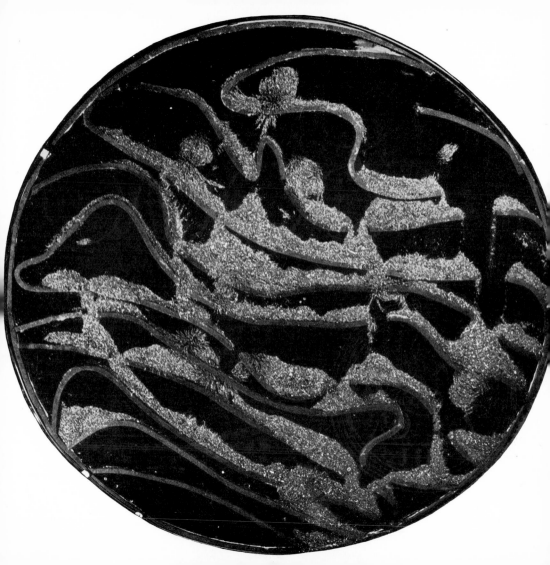

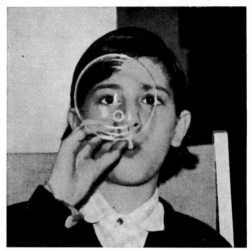

SOAP BUBBLE
One of the natural forms of the sphere.

The Baptistery of Pisa, one of the most beautiful structures on a circular base.

MAX BILL
Drawing obtained from a series of circles. 1942.

STOCK EXCHANGE

A circular trading post on the floor of the stock exchange.

GOOD SPIRITS

Magic circle to attract good spirits.

BOWLS

A game of bowls at Monte Olimpino.

BOTTICELLI

The Virgin with Child. Uffizi Gallery, Florence. The pictorial composition has been solved in such a way as to transform the round surface into the likeness of a sphere.

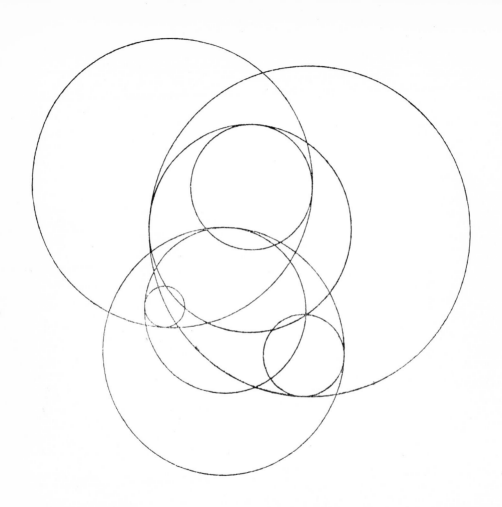

LANFRANCO BOMBELLI

Drawing, 1947.

ROUND HUT

The two oldest types of dwelling are built on a square or round plan. The domed hut is found in Australia and also among African and American tribes.

BALL-BEARING

MATAKAM HOUSE

At Mokolo, in the Cameroun, one finds the houses of the Matakams which consist of cylindrical mud rooms capped by straw cones. All the rooms together form a large enclosure. Each room has a precise function, and the number of rooms is determined by the size of the family. There is no opening to admit light from the outside and one must move around as in a dark circular labyrinth.

Enclosure for a family of nineteen people: rooms for the head of the family, for the bull, for the main wife, for the other wives and the children, for a married son, for another grown up son; also rooms for the water tank, for supplies, for the goats, for the ashes from which salt is made, and a kitchen - all surrounded by the enclosing wall. The Matakams keep the bull walled in his room; he can communicate with the exterior only through a small opening, very low and too small for him to go out. There is another opening for cleaning up th dung. The bull is thus kept for three years, fed and taken care of, and then on the occasion of the ancestral feast he is let out and killed in a solemn ceremony under the direction of the bull master.

CARDIOID

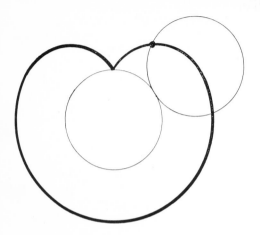

A curve described by a point situated on a circle which is made to roll without slipping around the circumference of another circle of equal diameter.

Astrological circles to calculate configurations.

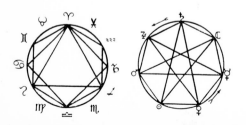

CYCLOID

The cycloid is the curve generated by a point on the circumference of a circle that is rolled along a straight line and kept always in the same plane. An interesting property of the cycloid was discovered by Galileo: with the help of the cycloid we can construct an area exactly equal to that of the given circle. Since the length of the cycloid from cusp to cusp is equal to four times the length of the diameter of the generating circle, we can demonstrate that the area which is bounded by the portion of the cycloid between the two cusps and the straight line which connects them is equal to three times the area of the circle. Therefore, if the circle is placed in the center of the figure, the space bounded by each side of the circle is exactly equal to the area of the circle itself.

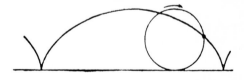

COMPASSES

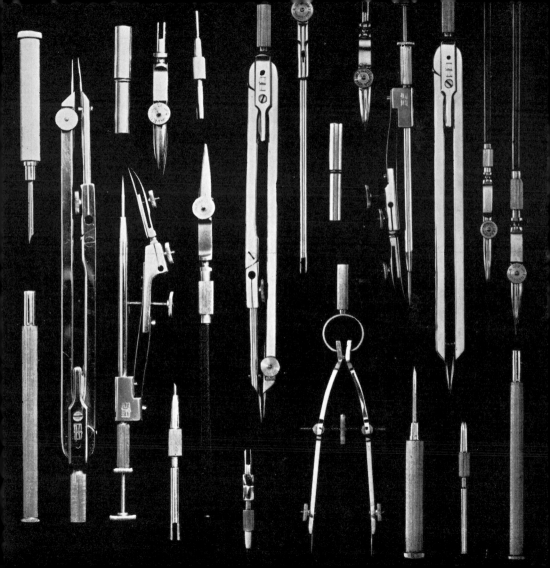

CURTATE CYCLOID

The curtate cycloid is the cycloid described when the generating point lies outside the circumference of the circle.

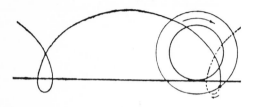

PROLATE CYCLOID

The prolate or inflected cycloid is the cycloid described when the point lies within the circumference.

CLEOPATRA

Magic circle of Cleopatra.

CYCLE

A concept introduced by Laguerre: the cycle is a circle with an arrow marked on its circumference. An equal circle with the arrow in the opposite direction is another, different cycle.

CLUSTERS OF SPHERES

The thickest reticular cluster of spheres is obtained when the centers of the spheres form a rhombohedric reticle.

POLYGONAL CIRCLES

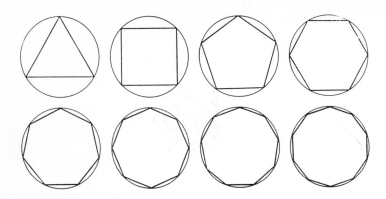

Circles with inscribed polygons. Analogous examples may be made for circumscribed polygons. This method of inscribing and circumscribing many-sided polygons was known to Archimedes who, by using polygons with 96 sides, demonstrated that π is less than 3 1/7 and more than 3 10/71. The value of π, from which the area of the circle is obtained, lies between these two figures.

OPPOSITION

Two circles touching each other, similar to two wheels which, in contact with each other, turn in contrary directions, symbolize opposition.

MAGIC CIRCLE OF THE COVENANTS

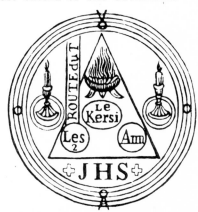

CONE-SPHERE

Model of experimental geometry executed in the School of Ulm.

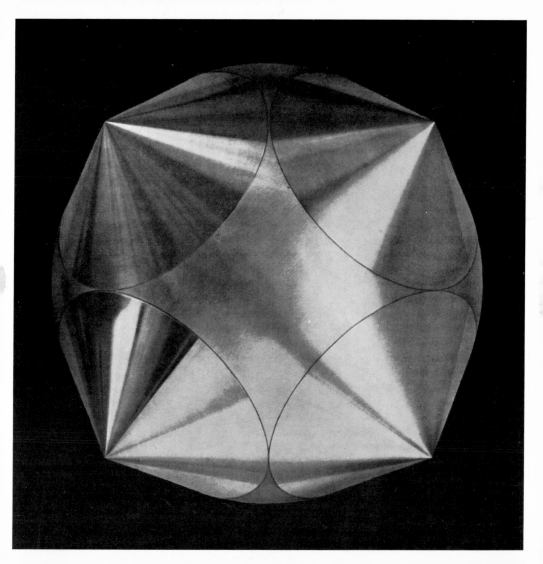

HORSE POWER

A wheel in which a horse, walking along its internal circumference, produces motive power used in ancient times to move the blades of river boats. In China dogs were used to move the wheels of small mills and prisoners were used to lift water for the irrigation of the fields.

CIRCLE

The circle is one of the oldest mathematical figures. The straight line is the simplest line, but the circle is the simplest curve.

CURVES TURNED INSIDE OUT

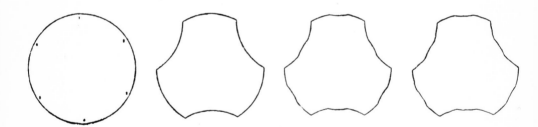

Draw a circle having any radius and choose six equidistant points on the circumference. Take three alternate arcs and turn them toward the inside. The perimeter will remain the same. Then cut in three each internal and external arc and invert the central section. By continuing this operation we will have a final curve with a perimeter equal to the original circle and an area equal to the inscribed hexagon.

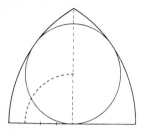

Inscribe a circle in a mixtilineal isosceles triangle.

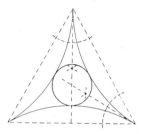

Inscribe a circle in a curvilinear equilateral triangle with three concave sides.

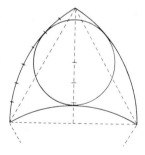

Inscribe a circle in a curvilinear equilateral triangle, of which two sides are convex and one is concave.

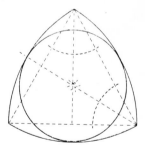

Inscribe a circle in a curvilinear equilateral triangle with three convex sides.

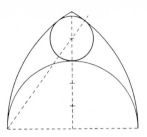

Inscribe a circle in a curvilinear triangle having as sides a semi-circle and two arcs whose radii are equal to the diameter of the semi-circle itself.

DECORATION

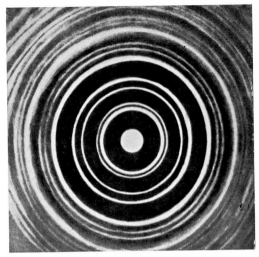

Electron diffraction through a very thin layer of silver. This proves the existence of a wave property in electrons, and therefore in matter.

DANCE

Dancing in a circle, stamping in rhythm, no one is first, no one is last - all are equal and all stamp alike. The dance begins slowly, then the rhythm takes hold and a sense of infinity arises from this human ring which turns round and round with its rhythmic beat. Photo by Michel Huet.

VILLARD DE HONNECOURT

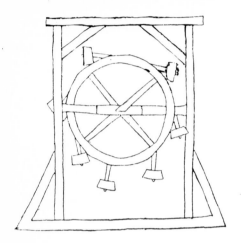

One of the first drawings of a machine for perpetual motion.

THE SUN-GOD

The adoration of the sun was part of the religion of ancient Egypt. The Sun - God, Amon-Râ, was represented by a falcon or by a man having a falcon's head, with a solar disk moving across the sky. An ancient Theban chant says: « Amon-Râ, divine falcon of the sparkling feathers, with a beating of his wings traces his circle on the vault of the heavens ». Amenophis IV, according to hieroglyphic readings, started a new cult with the adoration of the real sun and not the god Amon-Râ. From then on the divinity of the sun was represented simply by a disk with rays.

GOD

« God is a circle whose center is everywhere, but whose circumference is nowhere ». Ancient definition.

MAXWELL'S DISK

A disk, colored turquoise and red in various, adjustable sections. By rotating this disk one obtains a neutral gray. The neutral tone of gray is due to the right proportion of the two colors. If the quantity of red is larger one obtains a reddish gray; if the amount of turquoise is larger the gray tends toward a bluish green.

CHROMATIC DISK

Diagram of complementary colors arranged in a chromatic disk. The numbers marked by small squares indicate the relative positions of the colors on the natural spectrum; the numbers marked by crosses indicate the wave lengths in ten-millionths of a millimeter.

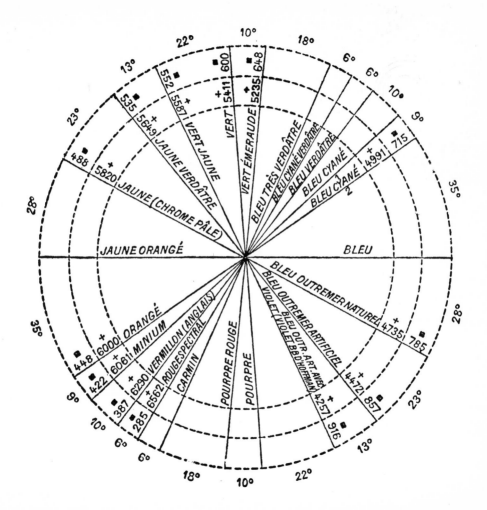

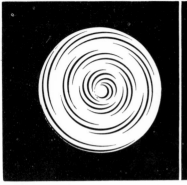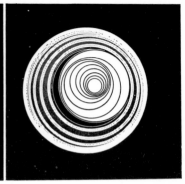

MARCEL DUCHAMP

Disks rotating at a constant speed with special optical effects, devised by Marcel Duchamp in 1936.

MOSLEM DECORATION

Moslem decoration in Istanbul.

NEWTON'S DISK

Disk divided into sections of various sizes with all the colors of the rainbow, four sections for each color. By rotating the disk at a certain speed all colors blend into a luminous white.

COMPOSITIONS

Some examples of figures obtained with circles, disks and parts of them.

ETERNITY

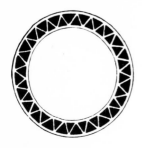

Oriental symbol of eternity.

The serpent biting its own tail is a symbol of eternity.

BENHAM'S DISK

Take a white disk and cover half of it with a deep black. On the other half paint concentric rings. By rotating this disk at a certain speed, instead of gray concentric rings we will see colored bands, dark and of low saturation. This leads to a disconcerting conclusion, that is, according to S.I. Vavilov, we cannot form a definition of light based simply on our visual perception.

ACOUSTIC EXPERIMENTS

Experiments have been made in the United States on the sound effects inside a sphere large enough to contain a person. The sound transmitted by the walls gives resonance to the whole human body: skull, thorax, abdomen, bones, all vibrate together. The man has the sensation that the sound originates in his own body. The resonance is activated to the utmost, and even if the man remains passive his body responds. Readiness to cooperate has little importance.

BUCKMINSTER FULLER

One of the many geodetic domes devised by Fuller. In 1957 this huge dome was set up in Honolulu in 22 hours for a series of concerts. All geodetic domes are built with pre-fabricated elements and are easily assembled. A few domes, hung on a cable, have been transported by helicopter. Fuller has built geodetic domes in the most varied materials: aluminum, plastic, wood; and at the Triennale Exhibition of Milan in 1954 he erected one of cardboard, having a diameter of 66 feet.

SPHERICAL BUILDINGS

Around the year 1770 Claude-Nicolas Ledoux planned a gigantic sphere as a symbol of eternity for the cemetery of Caux; he also designed a spherical house for the caretakers as a symbol of human loneliness. In 1800 Lequeu planned a spherical « Earth Temple ». Later on, the Russian composer Alexander Scriabin designed a semi-spherical edifice to be built over water, so that its reflection would complete the image of a whole sphere. This edifice was to be erected in India for a sacred performance of universal redemption. More recently, some Russian architects influenced by the futuristic movement designed a suspended spherical building to be used as a planetarium and reading room for the Lenin Institute. In March, 1958, Johann Ludovici presented a spherical house built of metal at a London exhibition.

EQUILIBRIUM

The three states of balance of a wheel: with the weight on top, unstable equilibrium; with the weight on the bottom, stable equilibrium; with the weight in the center, neutral equilibrium. Only in the first case may a spontaneous motion arise. Use is always made of this principle in the models of machines for perpetual motion.

CYLINDRICAL FOUNTAIN

The external cylinder, made of iron, has a diameter of 13 feet and a height of 6½ feet; it supports a number of curved blades, similar to those of a turbine, made of plastic.

The two internal cylinders are built in the same way. The external cylinder is operated by a slow motor and its colors are neutral from white to black. The medium cylinder turns with the wind and has warm, transparent colors from yellow to red and purple. The small cylinder is made to turn by a jet of water and its colors are cold from green to blue. The blending of all these colors in the rotations and casual combinations creates ever new and unexpected effects.

This fountain was built for the Montecatini Company at the Milan Fair in 1961.

SPHERICAL GEOMETRY

Lobachevski, in establishing his principles of non-Euclidean geometry, after describing the distance between two points as motion-constant, introduces the definition of the spherical surface as the locus of the points in space equidistant from a given point. The definition of a circle, or rather of a circumference, follows that of the spherical surface, since the circle is defined as the locus of the points common to two spherical surfaces. From this we come to the definition of a plane as the locus of the circles of intersection of equal spheres whose centers are two fixed points; these points are, at the same time, poles of the plane. In this way Lobachevski defines a limited portion of the plane, the portion inside the generating circle; but the infinity of the plane is potentially given as an extension of this area in all directions. Finally, the straight line is defined as the intersection of two planes; and the segment of a straight line is defined as a diameter common to two great circles of a sphere.

YELLOW AND BLUE

In his book * « Concerning the Spiritual in Art », or Kandinsky describes the optical effects of colors. He says that if we fill two equal circles, one with yellow and one with blue, and concentrate briefly on both of them, we have the impression that the yellow expands and gets nearer to us, while the blue develops a centripetal motion and seems to recede from us. In other words, our eyes are hit by the first circle, while they are drawn to the second.

TOYS AND GAMES

Many toys and games were born from the circle: the merry-go-round, circular dances, roulette, hoops, tops, balls, pin-wheels, and many others.

(*) George Wittenborn Inc., New York.

PEOPLE IN A CIRCLE

People form a circle spontaneously when they want to observe something together. This tendency probably gave rise to the arena, the circus, the trading posts in the stock exchange. Photo by Lori Sammartino.

Hindu cosmic diagram.

IGLOO

The Eskimos' house is a half-sphere of snow blocks. A long, open corridor which leads outside provides both ventilation and protection from cold winds. It is said that « a new hut is warmer than an old one because the new one is made of snow while an old one is made of ice ». It takes longer to build an igloo than to build a tropical hut. Nevertheless, the igloo is only a temporary dwelling for hunters because in Spring the snow on the roof begins to melt and water drips on the floor. This makes the igloo uninhabitable and it must be abandoned. Photo by Mario De Biasi.

JOSEPH

This problem is certainly one of the oldest and best known. There are many similar stories, and the people vary according to the epoch in which the story is laid. But the original story seems to be the one about a certain Joseph who found himself in a cave with forty other Jews determined to kill themselves rather than fall into the hands of the Romans. Joseph wanted to save his own life and that of a friend in the group. He placed all the people in a circle, reserving for himself and his friend the 16th and 31st place in the circle of 41 persons; and it was agreed that they would count by threes and that every third person would be killed. He and his companion remained the last ones and, later on, were also skillful enough to avoid punishment by the Romans.

Another version of this problem had 15 Turks and 15 Christians aboard a ship tossed around by a storm; the ship would sink if half of the men were not thrown into the sea. Having placed everyone in a circle, the Christians proposed that those would be sacrificed who, by counting by nines, would find themselves at the 9th, 18th place etc. Naturally the infidels were placed in such a way that all the Christians were saved.

Variations on Leonardo's principle of a perpetual motion machine based on free-moving spheres.

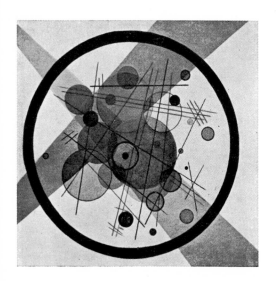

KANDINSKY

Circles within a circle. Painting, 1923. Collection of Louise and Walter Arensberg, Philadelphia Museum of Art.

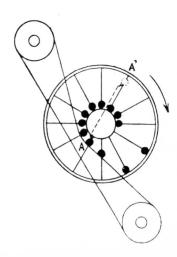

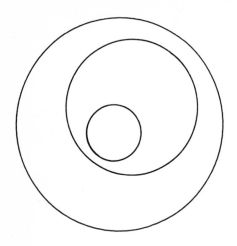

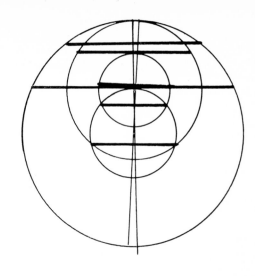

Movement and counter-movement.

Representation of the layers as the position of the center is changed. Each raising of the point of vision brings about the heightening of the horizon line.

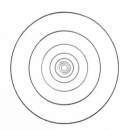

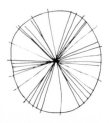

Sketches of energetic formation of the circle due to radiation from the center and to progressive growth of the radius from the inside to the outside.

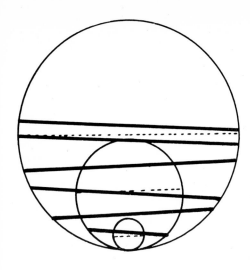

Synthesis of static and dynamic relationships.

FRANÇOIS MORELLET

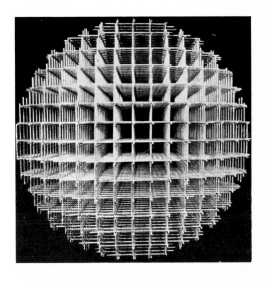

Spherical object obtained by soldering a number of metallic rods of different sizes at right angles. According to the point of observation the object appears as a sphere of cubic or hexagonal structure.

MANDALA

Symbol of totality. It has many versions: from the prehistoric « solar circle », to the circle which surrounds and protects, to the alchemistic microcosm, and finally to the modern symbol which encloses the psychic whole.

RING MACHINE

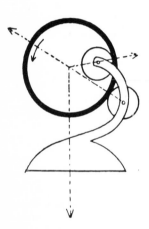

MICHELANGELO

The Holy Family. Uffizi Gallery, Florence.

An iron ring is held by two cylinders attached to a curved arm. The ring is free and, according to the inventor, would turn and thereby make the cylinders turn because the force of gravity would pull it down. But the center of gravity of the ring remains always at the same place and therefore the machine assumes a perfect and immobile balance.

BYZANTINE MONOGRAM

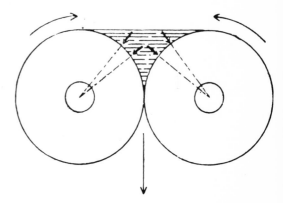

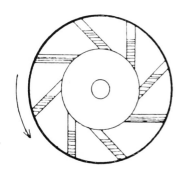

HYDROSTATIC MACHINE

Diagram for perpetual motion with liquid weight.

Two cylinders, in perfect contact with each other and rotating in contrary directions inside a sealed box. The upper space (shaded area) is filled with mercury which is supposed to exert pressure on the cylinders and make them rotate. In fact, every liquid exerts a pressure on the bottom of its container, but in this case the container has only walls and no bottom. Therefore, the pressure is exerted on the walls and, being directed toward the center of the cylinders, these remain still.

MACHINE WITH SPHERES

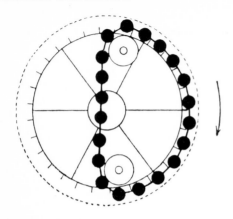

Machine for perpetual motion.
It was hoped that the weight of the spheres on the curve, being greater than the weight of the other spheres, would bring about motion.

Composition n. 383. Made of aluminum and laminated plastic, 27" x 9" x 8"; black, white and blue. 1959.

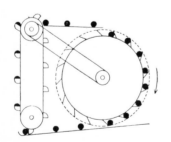

A variation of the same principle.

Sphere made of phenolic resin containing a cubic reticle. Structure n. 969, diameter 5".

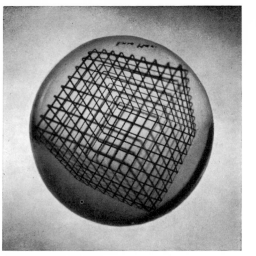
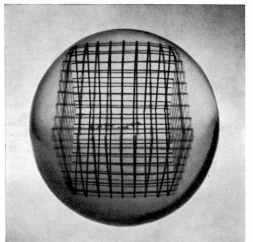
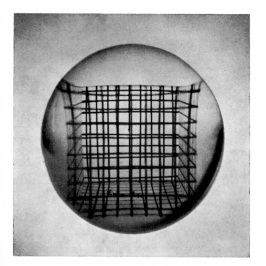
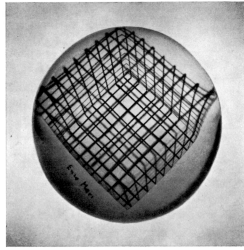

WATCH

The turning of the hands determines the most logical shape of this object.

NURAGHI

Ancient Sardinian constructions, built in the Bronze Age or perhaps earlier. Made of large stones on a circular base, they reach a height of nearly forty feet. The diameter, about twelve feet at the base, decreases as it goes up.

Some trade-marks and symbols, round or composed of circular elements.

EIGHT CIRCLES

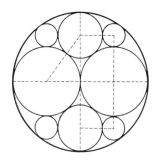

In a given circle inscribe eight circles of different dimensions, placed symmetrically and tangent to each other and to the given circle.

GIOTTO'S O

Giotto made « a marvelous painting in Pisa that gave him in that city and elsewhere so much fame that Pope Benedict IX, who intended to have some paintings made in St. Peter's, sent a member of his court from Trevisi to Tuscany to see what kind of man Giotto was and what his work was like. The Pope's envoy started out to see Giotto and to find out what other great masters of painting and mosaics there were in Florence. He first stopped in Siena, talked to many artists in that city and, having obtained some of their drawings, went on to Florence.

One morning he went to Giotto's shop and told him what the Pope had in mind. Then he asked Giotto, who was busy at work, to give him some drawing to send to His Holiness. Giotto, always very polite, took a sheet of paper and, with a brush dipped in red paint, holding his arm close to his side, made by hand a circle so perfect that it was a marvel to behold. Having done this, he said with a smile to the envoy: — Here is your drawing. — The papal representative thought that he as being fooled and asked: — Will I have any other drawing besides this? — This is even too much; — answered Giotto — send it with all the others and you will see that it will be appreciated.

« The envoy, seeing that he could not obtain anything else, left very unsatisfied and with the suspicion of having been duped. Nevertheless, when he sent all the drawings to the Pope, he also sent the one made by Giotto and explained the way in which the circle had been made, by hand and without any compass. The Pope and his art advisers clearly understood how far ahead Giotto was of the other painters. This story, when it became known, gave rise to an expression that is still in use when we say to dull-witted people: 'You are rounder than Giotto's O'. One must know that in Tuscany 'round' signifies not only a perfect circular figure, but also an obtuse mind.

« The Pope asked Giotto to come to Rome and, with great honor and recognition, entrusted to him the painting of five episodes of the life of Christ in St. Peter's, as well as the main work in the sacristy; and all these paintings were made by Giotto with such diligence that he never made a better one. In consequence, the Pope, recognizing that Giotto had served him well, paid him 600 gold ducats and showered him with so many favors that the whole of Italy talked about it ».

DEMONSTRATIVE OBJECT SKF

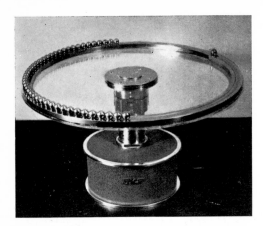

This large glass disk has a metal edge with a groove containing a number of steel balls. The disk is slightly inclined and rotates very slowly. From time to time a ball separates from the others and rolls down to join the first ball at the other end. Then another ball separates from the others, and so on and on...

INITIAL POINT

If we mark an initial point on the circumference of a circle we obtain a new figure which is used in the theory of complex functions.

GOLD

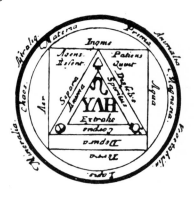

Magic circle used to make gold.

UMBRELLA

Japanese umbrella of bamboo and waterproof paper. The spokes of the umbrella are obtained from a single bamboo cane. When the umbrella is closed all the spokes fall back together in the shape of the cane and the umbrella is enclosed within it.

GESTALT PSYCHOLOGY

After having stared for a while at the center of this figure many observers will see another model. The radii which at first appeared as sides of the narrow sectors become the edges of the larger ones. It is clear that the arrangement of the model has changed and tends to change again. The rhythm with which the two arrangements alternate will gradually increase as one stares at the center of the figure.

ASTROLOGICAL PLANISPHERE

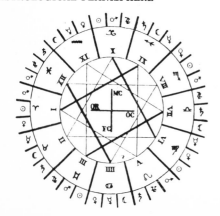

π

In the Book of Kings and in the Chronicles, π is given as equal to three. According to Egyptian mathematicians its value was 3.16. The decimal 3.1416 as known at the time of Ptolemy in the year 150 B.C.

PATHOCIRCLE

Another variation of the circle was introduced by an eminent American mathematician, C.J. Keyser, by taking a point away from a circle. This figure cannot be drawn because a point has no dimension, but it constitutes an important change of concept. Keyser called the new figure pathocircle, or pathological circle, and used it in the discussion of axioms of logic.

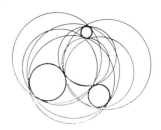

PROBLEM OF APOLLONIO

Given three circles, find the circle tangent to them. The problem is easily solved with ruler and compass; it has eight solutions.

CONCENTRIC WAVES

One of the natural forms of the circle.

POLAROID

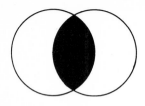

Graphic symbol of polaroid filters.

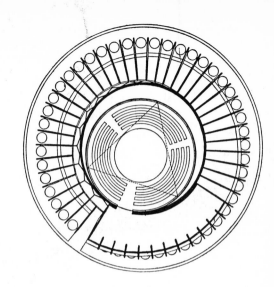

PSEUDOSPHERE

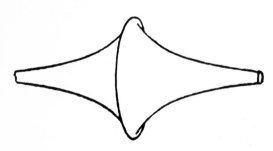

Geometric form determined by the rotation of a tractrix around a longitudinal axis. This tractrix is a curve perpendicular to a family of equal circles, placed at equal distances, whose centers are on a straight line.

PAFFARD KEATINGE CLAY

Plan of a building to be used for experimental presentations of dance, music, light effects; designed for the Carl Cherry Foundation in California.

X HOUR

Object of kinetic art, devised by Munari in 1945 and executed in fifty numbered copies by Danese in Milan. The half-disks in the center of the object are of transparent color and turn by clockwork, thus continually composing different geometrical figures.

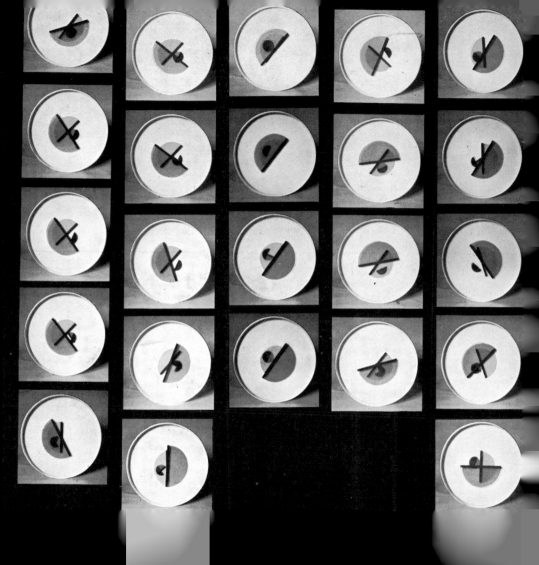

Drawings.

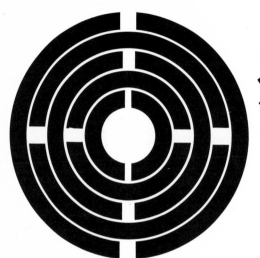

INDIAN BASKET

A flexible wire structure made of circular arcs. One may change its shape in various ways and obtain a number of geometrical figures.

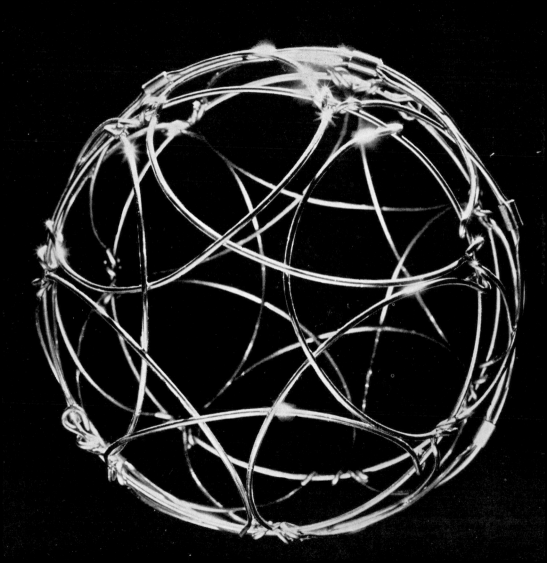

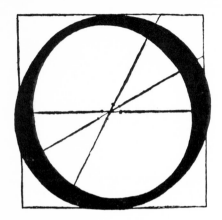

Letter of the « dignissimo antico » alphabet by Luca Pacioli.

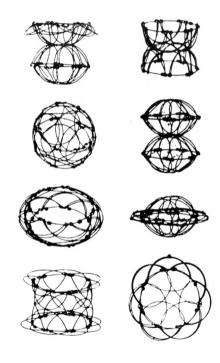

Variations in the shape of the Indian basket obtained by bending the object in various ways.

The Madonna of the Chair. Pitti Gallery, Florence.

Musical notation without beginning or end for a sound-giving object.

ROMANESQUE

Cross of Trinity Church in Caen.

BERNARD REDER

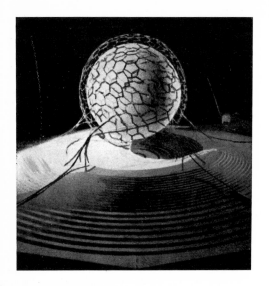

Spherical theatre. The spectators are ranged inside along a continuously moving spiral. The theatrical action takes place at the center of the sphere. The design calls for construction in materials of very light weight.

WHEEL

The first archaelogical evidence of the wheel goes back to the urban cultures of Mesopotamia. The oldest wheels consisted simply of massive disks of wood joined solidly to the axle which turned together with the wheels. At a later date hubs were invented and holes were made in the disks; these holes became larger and larger until the idea of spokes arose. Spoked wheels were already known in Asia Minor by 2700 B.C.

WHEEL AS A SYMBOL

The wheel as a symbol stands for the sun, divinity, good luck; it has always been used as an ornament. In ancient times the solstice was celebrated by rolling fiery wheels down the slopes and by throwing thin wooden disks into the air.

GOTHIC ROSE-WINDOW

Rose-window of the Basilica of Santa Chiara in Assisi. Photo by Paolo Monti.

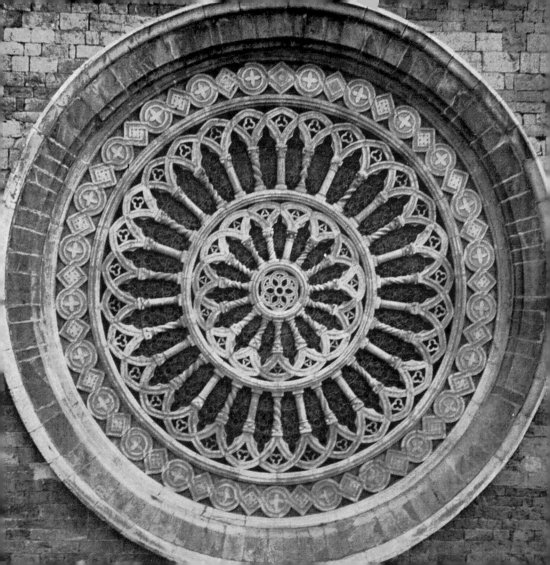

RADAR

The radar at the Vandenberg auxiliary station follows artificial satellites in their path through space. The network of radar stations extends from the Pacific coast of the U.S. to the Hawaiian Islands and north to Alaska.

CELTIC SEAL

DECREASING RADIUS

Draw a circle. In it draw an equilateral triangle. In the triangle inscribe another circle. In the second circle inscribe a square, and then follow with a pentagon. Continue in this way, always increasing the polygons by one side. It may seem that the radius of the circles becomes shorter and shorter, tending to zero. But it isn't so: the process of contraction tends to a limit which is reached when the polygon and the circle have become almost equal. The decreasing radius approaches a limit of about one twelfth of the radius of the original circle.

INCREASING RADIUS

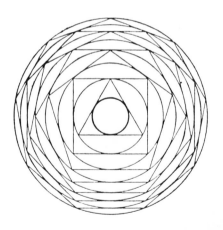

Closely related to the problem of the decreasing radius is the problem of the increasing radius, which consists of circumscribing polygons and circles instead of inscribing them.

In this case it may seem that the radius, increasing beyond any limit, becomes infinite. Instead, it approaches a limit of about twelve times the length of the radius of the original circle.

It is interesting to note that at the limit the increasing radius is the reciprocal of the decreasing one.

THE POTTER'S WHEEL

The turning wheel of the potter was known in Egypt before the beginning of the third millenium B.C. It was used by the craftsmen of Crete in the early period of the Bronze Age and it was known in many parts of India. It appeared in Europe around 500 B.C.

WRITING

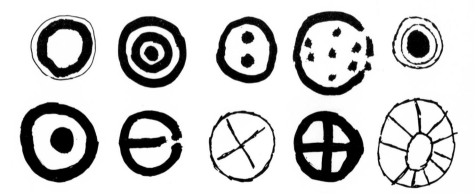

The circle is found at the origin of almost all the alphabets or ideograms. These signs are common to the writing of many prehistoric and ancient peoples in the East, in Europe, in America, in the Canary Islands.

CONNECTED SPHERES

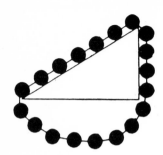

Search for perpetual motion by means of connected spheres. The larger number of spheres with their heavier weight on the longer arm was supposed to insure the motion.

Another version of motion by connected spheres.

EXPENDITURES

It seems that certain little disks which are sculptured on some pyramids and obelisks represent the money spent for these monuments. If the disks are arranged in a circle, it means that the monument was built with public funds; if, instead, they are in a line, it means that the disbursement was a private one.

A DREAM

In one of his books Carl Gustav Jung describes the following dream of one of his acquaintances: ... I recall the beauty of the sphere seen in its color of soft gray or opaque white against the night sky. When we realized that a terrific collision with the earth was about to occur, we were, of course, afraid. But it was a fear in which awe prevailed. It was a cosmic event which provoked a feeling of wonder and even reverence. While we were all rapt in that vision, there appeared a second sphere, and a third, and still others, approaching at great speed. Each sphere exploded on the earth like a bomb, but evidently at such a great distance that I could not ascertain the nature of the explosion, or detonation, or whatever it was. At least in one case I had the impression of having seen a flash of lightning. The spheres fell everywhere around us at intervals, but all so far away that we were unable to observe their destructive action. It seems as if there was a certain danger of shrapnel effect or something of the kind. Later — I must have returned home — I found myself talking to a girl seated on a cane chair...

SHINTO

A Shinto symbol: the revolving of the universe.

EMPIRE STYLE

Decorative design on a French fabric.

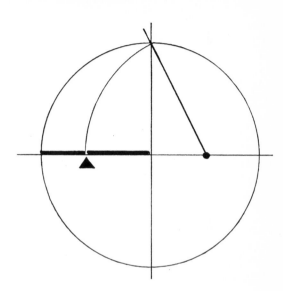

Construction of the golden section on the radius of a given circle.

STONEHENGE

Site of the famous ruins of a circular stone temple, erected about 1400 B.C. on Salisbury Plain, in England. It seems that the rough pilasters and architraves which compose the main circle, about 80 in number and weighing about 50 tons each, were not found nearby, but were brought from Prescelly. They were carried first for several miles from Prescelly to the nearest shore, then placed on rafts made of tree trunks and transported to a beach not far from Stonehenge, and finally brought by human toil to their final destination. Around the circular group of stones there are several circles of holes at equal distances from each other. Excavations brought to light implements and weapons of Irish origin, gold ornaments from Mycenae, amber objects from Central Europe, all of which shows the flourishing of trade with distant lands.

The central temple, still standing today, is a more recent circle, built of stones cut in nearer places. In the center of all these circles is a pilaster 16 feet high. It seems that the architect of the more recent structure at Stonehenge was an adventurous Greek who used the building experience of his people for this construction.

A COLUMN OF SPHERES

A mobile object in which the spheres, one on top of the other, are held by three glass panes. The sphere at the bottom lies on a gear of a very slow motor. All the spheres turn by friction and continuously change the combination of the white curved stripes painted on them. Munari 1962, Olivetti collection. Photo by Mulas.

KARLHEINZ STOCKHAUSEN

Karlheinz Stockhausen imagines an ideal auditorium for electronic music, shaped like a sphere. In the center of this sphere a platform is built in a manner which permits sound to pass through it; spectators stationed on it can listen to the music coming from all directions. Loud speakers are set all around the inside of the sphere.

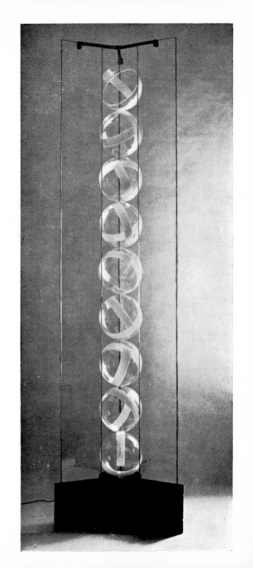

METEOROLOGICAL SIGNS

From left to right; clear sky, clouded sky, solar halo, lunar halo, rainbow, mirage, solar corona, lunar corona.

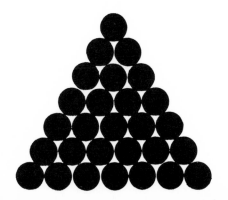

LAYER OF CIRCLES

This system of circles is based on a reticle formed with equilateral triangles. If at all the knots of the reticle we describe circumferences whose radii are half the length of the sides of the triangles, we obtain a system of circles which touch each other but are never on top of each other.

EQUAL AREAS

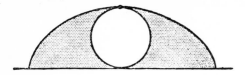

The two shaded portions have the same area as the circle which generated them.

SOLOMON

The great magic circle of Solomon.

SYMBOLS OF MARTYRDOM

CHINESE SPHERE

An ivory sphere containing eleven other spheres, one within the other, all carved from one solid piece by means of cone-tipped drills and other tools. All the spheres are free to move inside each other, from the smallest in the center to the largest on the outside.

TARGET PRACTICE

TURBINE

A turbine consists of an infinite number of continuous elements whose external parts are placed over a circumference, while their internal parts must all be equally inclined with respect to the circle. There is a whole geometry of turbines which deals with continuous groups of transformations connected with differential equations and with differential geometry, introduced by Edward Kasner.

MOSLEM TALISMAN

TRINITY

One of the symbols of the Trinity.

According to a Breton tradition the legendary knights of King Arthur sat at a round table to symbolize their equality and to make sure that none would seem more important than the others.

TRULLI

Ancient stone constructions, almost all one story high, built on a circular foundation and with a cone-shaped roof. The houses of more than one room consist of separate cylindrical constructions connected to each other by passages. The most famous Trulli are found at Alberobello and around Martina Franca, all in the Apulian region of Italy.

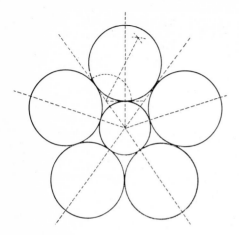

Draw several circles tangent to each other and to the outside of a given circle.

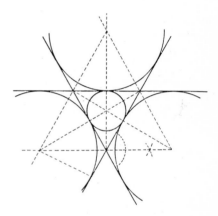

Draw four circles tangent to three straight lines which are symmetrically crossed.

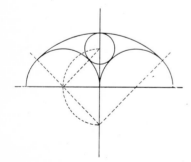

Inscribe a circle in a curvilinear isosceles triangle.

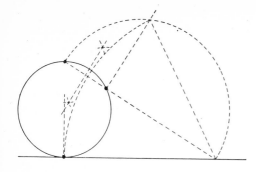

Given a straight line and two points outside of it, draw a circle which passes through these two points and a point on the straight line.

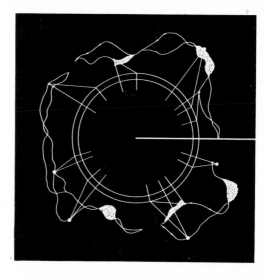

A circular gadget in which one can insert a series of sheets with musical notations. No beginning is indicated, and the sheets can be arranged in different ways, thus forming a number of variations based on a scheme by the Japanese composer Toru Takemitsu.

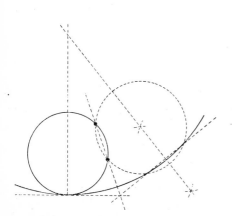

Draw a circle which passes through two given points on another circle.

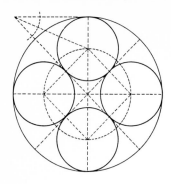

Draw several circles tangent to each other and to the inside of a given circle.

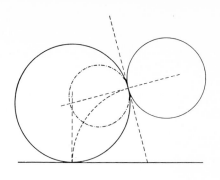

Draw a circle tangent to another at a given point and to a straight line at another given point.

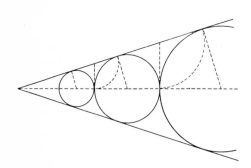

Circles tangent to each other and to the sides of a given triangle.

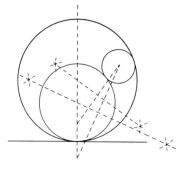

Draw two circles tangent to a straight line and to a given circle.

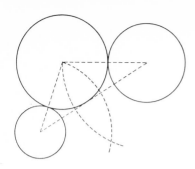

Draw a circle of a given radius, tangent to two other given circles.

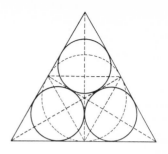

Draw three circles tangent to each other and internally tangent to a given equilateral triangle.

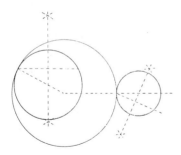

Given a circle with a fixed point on its circumference, and another point within or outside its circumference, draw another circle tangent to the first at the fixed point and passing through the other point.

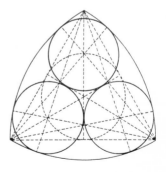

Draw three circles tangent to each other and internally tangent to a given curvilinear equilateral triangle.

Draw two tangents common to two given circles with different radii.

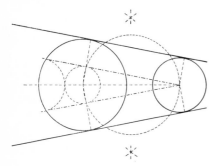

Solution A

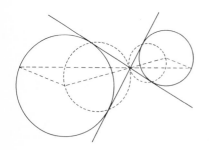

Solution B

ALL IS WELL

Sign of understanding among beggars.

MARY VIEIRA

Circle + movement = forms. Object of anodized aluminum, diameter 13 inches. Basle 1953-1958.

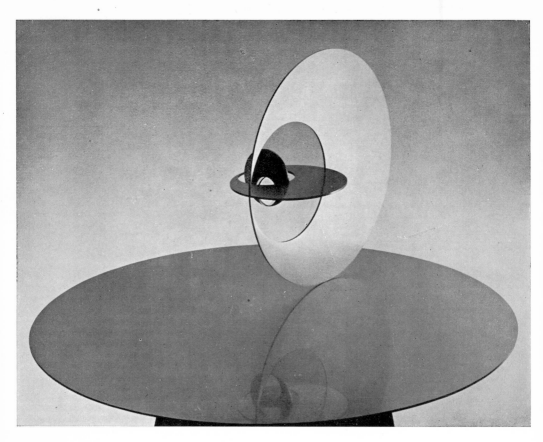

Circular mobile surfaces in their spherical
space. Structure of anodized aluminum,
Mary Vieira, Basle 1953-1958.

YANG - YIN

Some ancient Chinese sages, around the year 1000 B.C., observed that everything in nature is the result of the union of two opposing forces which they called Yang and Yin, and which they represented by a disk formed of two parts of equal shape but of different colors, such as black and white.

Each of these forces stands for a number of qualities and attributes: Yang is the positive force, representing masculinity, warmth, action, hardness, dryness, brilliancy, firmness, the essence of fire and light, the solid base of a hill, the source of a river..., while Yin is the negative principle, representing femininity, coolness, humidity, softness, darkness, mystery, secrecy, evanescence, nebulosity, turbidity, inaction, the essence of shadow and of water, the shady side of a hill, the mouth of a river... According to the prevalence of Yang or Yin things have different aspects: Yang is predominant in the heavens, while Yin predominates on the earth; in a single thing one principle may have prevalence at one time and the other principle at another time.

LUDOLPH VAN CEULEN

Famous German mathematician. In 1596 he calculated the value of π to 35 decimal places: 3.14159265358979323846 ...

According to his wish, this number was engraved on his tombstone at Leyden instead of a regular epitaph.

MARQUESS OF WORCESTER

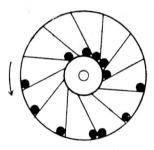

Model of a machine for perpetual motion. In 1663 the Marquess published a collection of his bizarre inventions; he then became famous for his sauce.

FAN

A series of equal radii determines the shape of this type of folding fan.

MONOCYCLE

American model.

Bibliography (titles of books and magazines are indicated in the language of the edition consulted by the author):

N. I. Lobacevskji: I NUOVI PRINCIPI DELLA GEOMETRIA. Einaudi, Torino.
S. I. Vavilov: L'OCCHIO E IL SOLE. Feltrinelli, Milano.
Steinhaus: MATHEMATICAL SNAPSHOTS. Oxford University Press, New York.
ENCICLOPEDIA DELLA CIVILTA' ATOMICA. Il Saggiatore, Milano.
Diringer: L'ALFABETO NELLA STORIA DELLA CIVILTA'. Barbera, Firenze.
Rudolf Koch. THE BOOK OF SIGNS. Dover Publications.
Ernst Lehner: THE PICTURE BOOK OF SYMBOLS. Penn, New York.
ARTE PROGRAMMATA. Olivetti, MILANO.
C. Malavasi: SETTECENTOCINQUANTA MECCANISMI. Hoepli, Milano.
Camillo Bruno: IL PROBLEMA DEL MOTO PERPETUO. Lavagnolo, Torino.
Paul Klee: TEORIA DELLA FORMA E DELLA FIGURAZIONE. Feltrinelli, Milano.
ENCYCLOPEDIE DE L'ORNEMENT. Albert Morancé, Paris.
Jung: SU COSE CHE SI VEDONO NEL CIELO. Bompiani, Milano.
Kasner e Newmann: MATEMATICA E IMMAGINAZIONE. Bompiani, Milano.
A. Speltz: LES STYLES DE L'ORNEMENT. Hoepli, Milano.
Julius E. Lips: L'ORIGINE DELLE COSE. Sansoni.
Pierre Schaeffer: A LA RECHERCHE D'UNE MUSIQUE CONCRETE. Ed. du Seuil, Paris.
Gyorgy Kepes: THE NEW LANDSCAPE. Paul Theobald, Chicago.
Huet et Fodeba: LES HOMMES DE LA DANSE. Edition Clairefontaine, Lausanne.
U. Eco e G.B. Zorzoli: STORIA ILLUSTRATA DELLE INVENZIONI. Bompiani, Milano.
IL MONDO DELLA NATURA. Mondadori, Milano.
R.W. Marks: THE DYMAXION WORLD OF BUCKMINSTER FULLER. Reinhold, N.Y.
Edouard Fer: SOLFEGE DE LA COULEUR. Dunod, Paris.
ARCHITECTURES FANTASTIQUES. L'architecture d'aujourd'hui, Paris.
SCIENTIFIC AMERICAN. New York.
Matila Ghyka: ESTETIQUE DES PROPORTIONS. Gallimard, Paris.
Siegfried Giedion: BREVIARIO DI ARCHITETTURA. Garzanti, Milano.
David Hilbert e S. Cohn-Vossen: GEOMETRIA INTUITIVA. Borighieri, Torino.
Kandinsky: CONCERNING THE SPIRITUAL IN ART. Wittenborn, N.Y.

Other Books published or distributed by George Wittenborn, Inc.

1018 Madison Avenue, New York, N. Y. 10021
and 91 Montgomery Street, Scarsdale, N. Y. 10583

Aalto (Alvar) Complete Works 1922-1960. over 600 ill. 1963 $18.50

Albers (Josef) *Poems and Drawings.* 22 ill. rev. ed. 1961 $7.50

Alloway (Lawrence) *Ettore Colla, Iron Sculpture.* 28 ill. 1960 $8.50

Alvard (Julien and S. Lupasco) *Frédéric Benrath.* 10 ill. 1959 $2.50

American Abstract Artists 1936-1966. Contributions by Albers, Bolotowsky, Kelpe, Lassaw, Mason, Morris, Shaw, Slobodkina and others, ill. 1966 $4.50

American Abstract Artists (Editors) *The World of Abstract Art.* 162 ill. 1957 $8.50

Annual of Architecture, Structure and Townplanning
>   Vol. 3 Ed. by the Association of Architects, Engineers and Townplanners, India, Honorary editor: Santosh Ghosh. 150 ill. 1963 $9.50
>   Vol. 4 400 ill. 1964 $9.50
>   Vol. 5 in preparation, ready 1967

Architecture: Formes & Fonctions. Ed. by Anthony Krafft
>   Vol. 9 1962-1963 250 p., ill., $9.50
>   Vol. 10 1963-1964 240 p., ill. $10.00
>   Vol. 11 1964-1965. 291 pp., ill. $11.00
>   Vol. 12 1965-1966. 238 pp., ill. $11.00

Art de France, Ed. by André Chastel
>   Vol. 1 488 pp., 500 ill. 1960 $17.50

Atchley (Dana) *ABC Design.* 32 silk-screened p., acetate stencil, limited ed. 1965 $9.00

Atelier 17, Hayter Print Group. 23 ill. 1949 $3.50

Baljeu (Joost) *Attempt at a Theory of Synthesist Plastic Expression.* 14 ill. 1964 $2.00

Barrett (Douglas) *Early Cola Bronzes (850-1014 A.D.)* 102 ill., 1965 $13.50

Baumann (Ernst) *New Gardens.* 500 ill. 1955 $11.50

Beckmann. Max Beckmann, ed. by J. B. Neumann and G. Franke, 48 ill. (Vol. 5 in the Art Lover Library), 1931 $1.50

Berne (Stanley) *The Dialogues.* 14 surrealist ill. by Matta. limited ed. 1962 $5.00
>   *The Multiple Modern Gods and Other Stories.* 8 woodcuts by Herman Zaage. 1964 $5.00

Blaser (Werner) *Structure and Form in Japan.* 205 ill. 1963 $15.00

Bolaffi's Catalogue of Modern Art 1966. 2000 ill. 1966 $40.00

Bosquet (Alain) *La Peinture de Dorothea Tanning.* 115 ill. 1966 $9.00

Brancusi: His Early Works: 1905-1908, by Geo. Bogza, ill. 1965 $10.00

Brandi (Cesare) *Burri.* 134 ill., folio, boxed 1964 $40.00

Branner (Robert) *La Cathédrale de Bourges et sa Place dans l'Architecture Gothique.* 138 ill. 1962 $10.00.

Brenson (Theodore) *Light into Color, Light into Space.* 15 ill. 1959 $2.50

Brongers (Georg A.) *Nicotiana Tabacum. The History of Tobacco Smoking in the Netherlands.* 167 ill., some in color, bibliog., 1964 $12.50

Bufano (Beniamino) *American Sculptor.* vol. 1 122 ill. 1957 $17.50
>   vol. 2 in preparation, ready end of 1967

Bullrich (Francisco) *Arquitectura Argentina Contemporanea.* 300 ill. 1964 $7.00

(Le) *Cabinet Fantastique*
>   Vol. 1: Projets et Divagations de C. N. Ledoux, Architecte du Roi, French text by Y. Christ.

Other Books published or distributed by George Wittenborn, Inc.

1018 Madison Avenue, New York, N. Y. 10021
and 91 Montgomery Street, Scarsdale, N. Y. 10583

80 ill. 1961 $10.00

Vol. 2: *Didier Barra et François de Nome dits, Monsu Desiderio,* French text by Dr. Félix Sluys. 114 ill. 1961 $12.50

Vol. 3: *Victor Hugo Dessinateur,* by Gaëtan Picon. 250 ill. 1964 $15.00

Vol. 4: *Bresdin,* by Claude Roger-Marx. 264 ill., 1966 $15.00

Callery (Mary) *Sculpture.* 172 ill. 1961 $15.00

Campigli (Massimo) *Scrupules.* 117 ill. 1957 $9.50

Carli (Enzo) *Il Duomo di Orvieto.* 267 ill. 1965 $67.50

Carver (Norman F.) *Silent Cities of Mexico and the Maya.* 170 ill., 16 drawings, 1965 $20.00

Ceroni (Ambrogio) *Modigliani: Dessins, Sculptures.* 222 ill. 1965 $15.00

Chermayeff (Ivan) *Blind Mice and Other Numbers.* over 50 ill. 1961 $3.50

Cirlot (Juan-Eduardo) *Lucio Fontana.* 37 ill. 1966 $4.00

Coburn (Alvin Langdon) *A Portfolio.* 16 ill. limited ed. 1962 $12.50

Cossio del Pomar (Felipe) *Peruvian Colonial Art: The Cuzco School of Painting.* 65 ill. 18 color plates, 1965 $10.00

Crispolti (E. and G. Marchiori) *Corrado Cagli.* 268 ill., 88 color plates, 1964 $37.50

Cuevas by Cuevas. 100 ill. 1965 $5.00

(The) Dada Movement (Galleria Schwarz, Milan)

1. *Arman, Raysse, Spoerri, Dufrene, Rotelfo, Villegle.* 94 ill. 1966 $1.50
2. *Dada in Italy.* in prep. 1966 $1.50
3. *'Round the World with Dada.* in prep. 1966 $1.50
4. *The Protagonists: Dada is 50 Years Young.* in prep. 1966 $1.50
5. *Towards a Cold Poetic Image.* in prep. 1966 $1.50

De Angelis D'Ossat (G. and C. Pietrangeli) *Il Campidoglio di Michelangelo.* 49 ill., over 100 drawings, plans, 1965 $95.00

De Bock (Paul Aloise) *Paul Delvaux: Der Mensch, Der Maler.* 56 ill. 1965 $8.50

Degas (Edgar) *Huit Sonnets.* 19 ill. 1947 $4.00

Denby (Edwin) *Mediterranean Cities.* 30 ill. 1956 $7.50

Dereux (Philippe) *Raymond Grandjean.* 10 ill. 1959 $2.50

Deroudille (René) *René Laubiès.* French text 10 ill. 1957 $3.00

Documenti D'Arte D'Oggi, Ed. by the mac espace group in Milan, Italy

Vol. 3 1955-1956, 110 ill. $12.50

Vol. 4 1956-1957, 160 ill. $12.50

Vol. 5 1957-1958, 100 ill. $12.50

Documents of Modern Art Series. See: Cover page

Dooijes (D. and P. Brattinga) *History of the Dutch Poster.* 350 ill. 1966 c. $28.00

Due Dimensioni. A dictionary of contemporary Italian commercial designers, text in 4 languages, edited by Max Huber et al, 2700 ill. 1965 $30.00

Duthuit (Georges) *Le Serpent dans la Galère.* 34 ill. 1945 $15.00

Far Eastern Antiquities Museum, Stockholm. Details on request

Bulletin No. 36, 250 pp., 75 ill. 1964 $14.75

Bulletin No. 37, 254 pp., 81 ill. 1965 $14.75

(Le) Fauconnier. Text by Ozenfant, ed. by J. B. Neumann, 9 ill. 1949 $1.00

Other Books published or distributed by George Wittenborn, Inc.

1018 Madison Avenue, New York, N. Y. 10021
and 91 Montgomery Street, Scarsdale, N. Y. 10583

Feldman (Eugene) *New York: West Side*. Fold-out plate in end boards, limited ed. 1965 $50.00

Focillon (Henri) *The Life of Forms In Art*. 19 ill. reprint 1966 $2.50

Four Great Makers of Modern Architecture. Gropius, Le Corbusier, Mies van der Rohe, Wright. Symposium held at Columbia University School of Architecture in 1961. 1964 $7.50

Gallatin (A. E.) *Paintings of A. E. Gallatin*. 40 ill. 1948 $2.50

Gangoly (O. C.) *Indian Terracotta Art*. 50 ill. 1959 $9.00

Gasparini (Graziano)

    La Arquitectura Colonial de Coro. ill. 1961 $20.00

    La Arquitectura Colonial en Venezuela. ill. 1965 $30.00

    La Casa Colonial Venezolana. 149 ill. 1962 $7.50

Gaudi (Antonio) Preface by Le Corbusier. 61 ill. 1958 $7.50

George (Waldemar) *Hilaire Hiler and Structuralism: New Concept of Form-Color*. 8 ill. 1958 $2.50

Gindertall (R. V.) *Morice Lipsi*. 104 ill. 1965 $15.00

Gleizes (Albert) *Le Cubisme 1908-1914. Cahiers. Vol. 1: Souvenirs*. ill. 1957 $3.00

Goeritz. *Mathias Goeritz*, by Olivia Zuniga. 190 ill. 1963 $7.00

Green (Samuel Adams) *Andy Warhol*. 27 ill. 1965 $7.50

Gregory (Albert) *Color in Line*. 16 ill., limited ed. 1960 $40.00

Haass (Terry and Ferrand, Michel) *Germinal*. 6 orig. color etchings. 1957 $100.00

Hammer (Victor) *Memory and Her Nine Daughters*. 1957 $15.00

Henze (Anton) *La Tourette: The Le Corbusier Monastery*. 48 photos by B. Moosbrugger, 1966 $4.50

Herzka (Dorothy) *Pop Art*. 27 ill. 1965 $3.00

Honegger (Gottfried) *Fiktion und Realität erster Versuch einer Zusammenfassung meines heutigen Standortes in 24 Texten*. 5 orig. lithographs. 1956 $25.00

Honegger-Lavater (Warja) *Folded stories*. Original lithographs in numbered editions.

    2. *Die Grille und die Ameise* (The Grasshopper and the Ant) $3.50

    3. *Match* $3.50

    4. *Die Party* $3.50

    5. *La Promenade en Ville* $3.50

    6. *Rape of the Sabines* $3.75

    7. *Passion and Reason* $3.75

    8. *The Good Intention is Blue* $4.50

    9. *Night and Day and Night . . . and Day and Night* $4.50

    10. *Extra-ordinary Lemuel* $4.50

Hostettler (Rudolf) *Technical Terms of the Printing Industry*. 3rd rev. ed. 200 ill. 1959 $4.00

Howarth (Thomas) *Charles Rennie Mackintosh and the Modern Movement*. 250 ill. 1953 $12.50

Ioannou (A. S.) *Byzantine Frescoes of Euboea*. Vol. 1 100 ill. 1959 $10.00

Jenkins (Paul) *Seeing Voice, Welsh Heart*. 17 poems by Cyril Hodges, 6 original color lithos, limited ed., 1965 $150.00

Kahn (Louis I.) *The Notebooks and Drawings of Louis I. Kahn*. over 100 ill. 1962 $14.50

Kahnweiler (D. H.) *Pour Daniel-Henry Kahnweiler*. 42 ill., 8 color lithos by Mourlot, 1965 $35.00

Kent (Adaline) *Autobiography*. 78 ill. 1958 $5.00

Kinetic Art. Four essays by Stephen Bann, Reg Gadney, Frank Popper and Philip Steadman. 80 ill. 1966 $3.00

Other Books published or distributed by George Wittenborn, Inc.

1018 Madison Avenue, New York, N. Y. 10021
and 91 Montgomery Street, Scarsdale, N. Y. 10583

Le Corbusier *Complete Works*. 1910-1960 800 ill. reprint ready 1967

        Vol. 1: 1910-1929, 400 ill. 1960 $15.00
        Vol. 2: 1929-1934, 400 ill. 1964 $15.00
        Vol. 3: 1934-1938, 400 ill. 1964 $15.00
        Vol. 4: 1938-1946, 400 ill. 1961 $15.00
        Vol. 5: 1946-1952, 400 ill. 1955 $15.00
        Vol. 6: 1952-1957, 500 ill. 1957 $15.00
        Vol. 7: 1957-1962, 500 ill. 1965 $18.50

Lehmbruck. *Die Druckgraphik von Wilhelm Lehmbruck*, by Erwin Petermann. 239 ill. 1964 $45.00

(Louise) Leiris Gallery Exhibition Catalogues, ill.

Series A:

    1. *Pablo Picasso: Peintures, 1955-1956* $3.50
    2. *Andre Masson: Peintures récentes et anciennes* $4.50
    3. *A Beaudin: Peintures, 1927-1957* $2.50
    4. *Juan Gris: Peintures de 1926 et 1927* $4.50
    5. *E. de Kermadec: Peintures 1927-56* $4.50
    6. *Fernand Leger: Dessins et Gouaches* $4.50
    7. *Suzanne Roger: Peintures 1923-1958* $2.50
    8. *Henri Laurens: Sculptures en pierre* $2.50
    9. *Elie Lascaux: Peintures 1921-1959* $4.50
    10. *Picasso: Les Ménines 1957* $4.50
    11. *Picasso: 45 gravures sur linoleum, 1958-1960* $4.50
    12. *Picasso: Dessins 1959-1960* $3.50
    13. *Y. Rouvre: Peintures 1951-1961* $2.50
    14. *Picasso: Peintures (Vauvenargues 1959-1961)* $4.50
    15. *A. Masson: Peintures 1960-1961* $4.50
    16. *Picasso: "Déjeuner sur l'Herbe" de Manet* $4.50
    17. *Picasso: Peintures 1962-1963*   (now out of print)

Series B:

    1. *D.-H. Kahnweiler: 50 Ans d'Edition* $3.50
    2. *A. Masson: Dessins, 1960* $2.50
    3. *Manolo: Sculptures-Gouaches-Dessins* $4.50
    5. *Juan Gris: Dessins* $4.50
    6. *Henri Laurens: Terre-Cuites (Clay Sculptures)* $2.50
    7. *A. Beaudin: Sculptures* $2.50

Lewis (David) *Mondrian. His Paintings*. 10 ill. 1957 $2.50

    Constantin Brancusi. 65 ill. 1958 $3.50

Leymarie (Jean) *Marc Chagall Monotypes, 1961-1965*. 25 color ill., limited ed. 1966 $42.50

Macagy (Douglas) *James Boynton*. 14 ill. 1959 $3.95

Madsen (Stephan Tschudi) *Munch's Wall Paintings*. 13 ill. 1959 $1.00

Maechler (René and Georges Thonet) *Paesaggi di Donna*. 35 photographs of the nude, 1965 $12.50

Marchiori (Giuseppe) *Jean Arp 1913-1963*. 95 ill. 1963 $20.00

Other Books published or distributed by George Wittenborn, Inc.

1018 Madison Avenue, New York, N. Y. 10021
and 91 Montgomery Street, Scarsdale, N. Y. 10583

Marchiori (Giuseppe) *Quinto Ghermandi*. 45 ill. 1962 $4.50
Masson (André) *Mythology of Being*. limited ed. 9 ill. portfolio. 1942 $25.00
     Nocturnal Notebook 16 ill. 1944 $3.00
Mathieu (Georges) *From the Abstract to The Possible*. 21 ill. 1960 $3.50
Medieval Wooden Sculpture in Sweden
  Vol. 1: *Attitudes to the Heritage*. ill. 1964 $8.50
  Vol. 2: *Romanesque and Gothic Sculpture*. ill. 1966 $9.50
  Vol. 3: *Late Medieval Sculpture*. ill. 1966 $9.50
  Vol. 4: *Catalogue*. ill. 1966 $17.50
  Vol. 5: *Plates*. 1964 $35.00
Mercandino (Cesare) *Impianti Sportivi*. 2 vols., ill. 1965 $40.00
Miranda (Salvador) *Les Palais des Empereurs Byzantins*. 34 ill., limited ed. 1965 $10.00
Modern Artists In America, Ed. by R. Motherwell, Ad Reinhardt, B. Karpel. 160 ill. 1952 $8.50
Monet (Claude) by Adrian Stokes, 8 color plates. 1958 $2.50
Moore (Henry) *Sculpture & Drawings:*
  Vol. 1. 1921-1948. 254 ill. 1957 $15.00
  Vol. 2. 1949-1954. 195 ill. reprint, 1965 $15.00
  Vol. 3. 1955-1964. 148 ill. 1965 $15.00
     Stone and Wood Carvings 1922-1961. 57 ill. 1961 $4.00
Moscanyi (Paul) *Karl Knaths*. 60 ill. 1958 $5.00
Mroszczak (Jozef) *Polnische Plakatkunst* (The Polish Poster In Art) 377 ill. 1962 $16.50
Muehsam (Alice) *German Readings 2: A Brief survey of art from the middle ages to the twentieth
  century for students of German and fine arts*. 2nd rev. ed. 1965 $3.50
Munari (Bruno) *The Circle*. ill. 1966 $4.50
     The Square. ill. reprint 1966 $4.50
     Good Design. ill. 1964 $1.50

New Furniture
  Vol. 4: 1956-1958. 347 ill. 1958 $12.50
Novelli (Gastone) *Antologia del Possible*. ill. 1962 $4.00
Of Art, Plato To Picasso. Ed. by A. E. Gallatin. 3 ill. 1963 $2.00
Otto (Frei) *Zugbeanspruchte Konstruktionen* (Shell Constructions)
  Vol. 1: *Pneumatische Konstruktionen Berechnung der Membranen, Zugverankerungen im Bau-
     grund*. ill. 1962 $38.50
  Vol. 2: *Grundbegriffe und Uebersicht der Konstrucktionen, Berechnung von Seilen, Seilnetzen
     und Seilwerken*. ill. 1966 $25.00
  Vol. 3: *Spannweiten, Ideen und Versuche zum Leichtbau. Ein Werkstattbericht von Conrad
     Roland*. ill. 1965 $15.00
Picasso (Pablo) *Guernica*. 33 ill. 1956 $1.50
     Lithographs 1945-1948. 67 ill. 1948 $3.00
Pirelli (Giulia and Carlo Orsi) *Milano*. 54 photos. 1965 $15.00
Ponente (Nello) *Mastroianni*. ill., limited ed., 1963 $27.50

Other Books published or distributed by George Wittenborn, Inc.

1018 Madison Avenue, New York, N. Y. 10021
and 91 Montgomery Street, Scarsdale, N. Y. 10583

(Les) Primitifs Flamands
- Vol. 4: *New England Museums,* by Colin T. Eisler. ill. 1961 $13.50
- Vol. 5: *Le Musée National de Louvre,* by Helene Adhemar. ill. 1962 $15.50
- Vol. 6: *La Chapelle Royale de Grenada,* by Roger von Schoute. ill. 1963 $18.50
- Vol. 7: *Le Palais Ducal D'Urbin,* by Jacques Lavalleye. ill. 1964 $20.00
- Vol. 8: *Le Musée de l'Ermitage,* by Vladimir Loewinson-Lessing and Nicolas Nicouline. ill. 1965 $17.50
- Vol. 9: *Les Musées de Pologne.* in prep.   1966

Problems of Contemporary Art Series. See: Cover page
Rand (Paul) *Trademarks.* 1960 $10.00
   Thoughts On Design. 94 ill. $15.00
Read (Herbert) *Kandinsky 1866-1944.* 8 ill. 1959 $2.50
Redig de Campos (D.) *Raffaello Nelle Stanze.* 73 color plates, 1965 $45.00
Rety (Louis) *Fely Mouttet, Peintre.* 12 ill. 1958 $2.00
Reynal (Jeanne) *The Mosaics of Jeanne Reynal.* 81 ill. 1964 $15.00
Richter (Hans and Herbert Read) *Hans Richter.* 144 ill. 1965 $19.50
Rodin, Auguste) *A la Venus de Milo.* Fr. text. 6 ill. 1945 $4.00
Roesch (Kurt) 9 Engravings to accompany "The Sonnets to Orpheus" by Rainer Maria Rilke. 35 numbered and signed copies. 1944 $250.00
Rosenthal (Erwin) *The Changing Concept of Reality in Art.* 46 ill. 1962 $6.50
Ruscha (Edward) *Twenty Six Gasoline Stations.* 26 photos, 1962 $3.00
   Various Small Fires. 20 photos, 1964 $3.00
   Some Los Angelos Apartments. 40 photos of exteriors, 1965 $3.00
Sauvage (Tristan) *Nuclear Art.* Essays, manifestoes, 213 ill. 1962 $17.50
Schoofs (Rudolf) *Engravings.* Vol. 1. 22 ill. 1960 $2.50
   Engravings. Vol. 2. 16 ill. 1963 $4.50
Seuphor (Michel) *Lee Hersch, Abstract Artist.* 12 ill. 1954 $2.50
Shorr (Dorothy C.) *The Christ Child in Devotional Images In Italy during the 14th Century.* 450 ill. 1953 $6.50
Stahly (François) *François Stahly.* 84 ill. 1962 $6.50
Steinberg (Leo) *Jasper Johns. A critical study.* 30 ill. 1963 $3.50
Sweeney (James Johnson) *Afro (Basaldella) Paintings, Gouaches, Drawings.* 34 ill. 1961 $20.00
   The Miro Atmosphere. 93 ill. 1959 $7.50
   Same, with one signed orig. color litho. $75.00
Taillandier (Yvon) *Creation Miro 1961.* 60 ill. 1962 $9.00
Tanguy (Yves) *Catalogue of the Paintings of Yves Tanguy.* 462 ill. 1963 $37.50
Tapie (Michel) *Antonio Tapies.* 46 photographs. 1959 $7.50
Tapies. *Antoni Tapies,* by Blai Bonet. Spanish text, ill. 1965 $54.50
   Observations. 8 ill. 1956 $3.50
   Claire Falkenstein. 19 ill. 1959 $5.50
Teshigahara (Sofu) *Portfolio.* 31 ill. $9.00
   Sculpture, 1957-58. 27 ill. $6.00

Other Books published or distributed by George Wittenborn, Inc.

1018 Madison Avenue, New York, N. Y. 10021
and 91 Montgomery Street, Scarsdale, N. Y. 10583

Trans/Formation: arts, communication, environment, Ed. by H. Holtzman
      Vol. 1, No. 1 1950 $3.50
      Vol. 1, No. 2 1951 $3.50
      Vol. 1, No. 3 1952 $3.50
Trucchi (Lorenzo) *Jean Dubuffet.* Italian text, 360 ill. 1965 $45.00
Tselos (Dimitri) *The Sources of the Utrecht Psalter Miniatures.* 361 ill. 1960 $20.00
Vasarely. *Victor Vasarely,* by Victor and Marcel Joray. ill. 1965 $27.50
Villani (D.) *Storia del Manifesto Pubblicitario.* History of the Poster. 900 ill. 1965 $36.00
Werbeform (German Graphic Annual).
      Vol. 3: German-Eng. text, 1000 ill. 1962 $20.00
Weston (Edward) *The Daybooks of Edward Weston.* Vol. 1: Mexico. 40 ill. 1962 $10.00
Wilke (Ulfert) *One, Two and More.* portfolio, limited ed. 1960 $20.00
            Fragments from Nowhere. 19 facsimiles. 1960 $20.00
Wurman (Richard Saul) *Various Dwellings Described in a Comparative Manner.* 35 drawings by
      students of University of North Carolina School of Design, 1964 $7.00
Young (Dennis and Barbara) *Furniture in Britain Today.* 310 ill. 1964 $10.50
Zannas (Eliky) *Khajuraho.* 176 ill. 1961 $47.50
Zekowski (Arlene) *Concretions.* 13 ill. by Milton Avery, limited edition. 1962 $5.00
        Abraxas. 8 woodcuts by Herman Zaage, 1964 $5.00